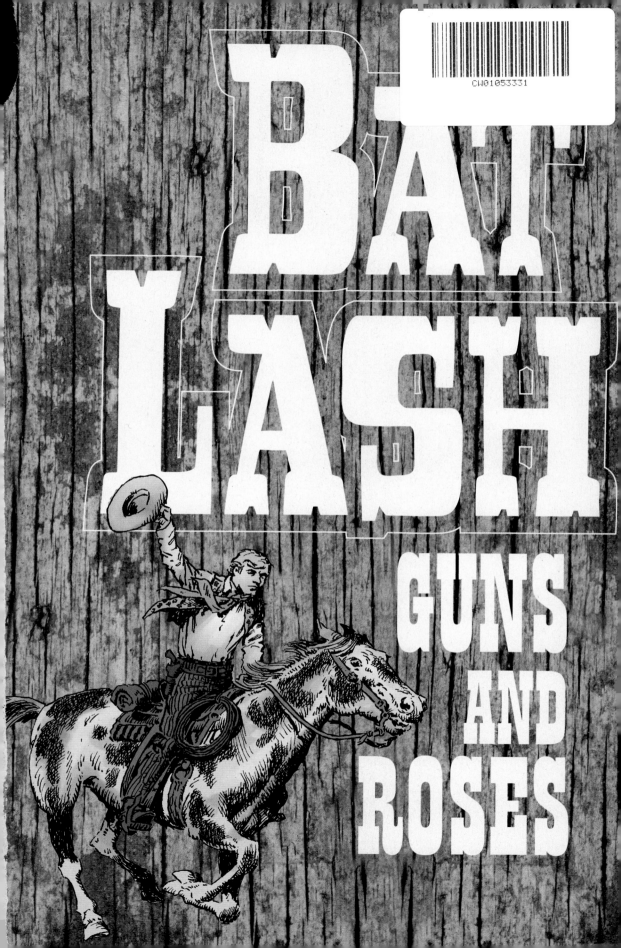

# BAT LASH
## GUNS AND ROSES

**Sergio Aragonés**
**Peter Brandvold**
Writers

**John Severin**
Artist

with Javi Pina
and Steve Lieber
(pages 135-140)

**Steve Buccellato**
Colorist

**Pat Brosseau**
Rob Leigh
Letterers

**Walter Simonson**
Original Series Covers

Cover by Nick Cardy and Kevin Nowlan.

**BAT LASH: GUNS & ROSES**
Published by DC Comics. Cover, text and compilation
Copyright © 2008 DC Comics. All Rights Reserved.

Originally published in single magazine form in BAT LASH
1-6. Copyright © 2008 DC Comics. All Rights Reserved.
All characters, their distinctive likenesses and related
elements featured in this publication are trademarks of
DC Comics. The stories, characters and incidents featured
in this publication are entirely fictional. DC Comics does
not read or accept unsolicited submissions of ideas,
stories or artwork.

DC Comics, 1700 Broadway, New York, NY 10019
A Warner Bros. Entertainment Company
Printed in Canada. First Printing.
ISBN: 978-1-4012-1943-7

GUNS AND ROSES
CHAPTER 1:
SPLENDOR IN THE SAGE
IF YOU CAN CATCH ME, BAT LASH...!
SEVERIN
A THING OF BEAUTY IS A JOY FOREVER: ITS LOVELINESS INCREASES; IT WILL NEVER PASS INTO NOTHINGNESS.
-John Keats

HEY, BRUBAKER, AIN'T THAT YOUR GIRL DOMINIQUE RIDIN' WITH THAT MUSTANGER'S BOY?

WHAT THE HELL'RE YOU TALKIN' ABOUT, SCRATCH?

BETTER HAVE A LOOK AT THIS.

IT'S THAT MUSTANGER'S BOY, AIN'T IT? WHAT'S HIS NAME?

BAT LASH!

I DON'T WANT TO GO BACK TO THE RANCH. I WANT TO STAY WITH YOU FOREVER, BAT.

WE'LL BE TOGETHER SOON, DOMINIQUE. SOMEHOW, WE'LL WORK IT OUT.

PROMISE?

PROMISE.

♪ SHE WON MY HEART WHEN SHE SMILED AT ME... ♪

♪ THROUGH THE BEAMS OF THE ROSY MAY MORN... ♪

WHOA!

WHAT THE HELL...?

LOOK WHAT I CAUGHT IN THAT DRIED-UP RIVER, BOYS!

LET'S TAKE 'IM FOR A RIDE!

LET ME GO, YA FORK-TAILED DEVIL!

WE GONNA DRAG HIM TILL HE'S NEKKID, SHERIFF, LIKE WE DONE WITH THEM RUSTLERS LAST WEEK?

BAT LASH, I'M GONNA STRETCH YOUR NECK SO FAR THAT THOSE RANGE-CLUTTERIN' FOLKS OF YOURS ARE GONNA THINK YOU'RE A BIG OL' DIAMONDBACK!

THEY AIN'T GONNA KNOW WHETHER TO BUILD HIM A WOODEN OVERCOAT OR TOSS HIM INTO THE STEW POT!

I HAVEN'T STOLEN OR LONG-LOOPED ANY BEEF, AND YOU KNOW IT, BRUBAKER!

HAY-YA-YAAA

COMANCHES!

AHHH!

LIGHT A SHUCK, BOYS! THOSE DAMN DOG-EATERS GOT US OUTNUMBERED!

LAW, LAW, I GOTTA BE THE FIRST TEXAN TO BE RELIEVED AT THE SIGHT OF A COMANCHE WARRIOR!

15

BUDADADUMMDUMM

CRACK!

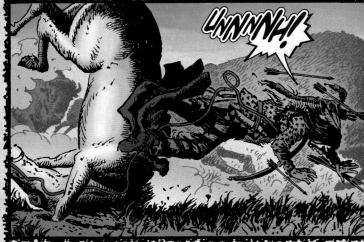

UNNNN!

BUDADADUMMDUMM

BUDADADUMMDUMM

"LATER, HE BUILT A FIRE..."

THIS IS GOING TO HURT, SO I'LL COUNT TO *THREE*. GET READY...

"...AND REMOVED THE ARROW..."

...ONE!

UGHH!

EASY, FELLA. I'LL GET YOU BACK TO YOUR PEOPLE QUICK AS I CAN.

"...AND SAVED MY LIFE."

WHY DEPRIVE THE RICH RANCHER'S DAUGHTER OF THE PLEASURE OF RUNNING HER HANDS THROUGH HIS HAIR...?

...WHEN HE HAS SO LITTLE ELSE TO PLEASE HER WITH!

WHO SAYS THE COMANCHES HAVE NO SENSE OF HUMOR?

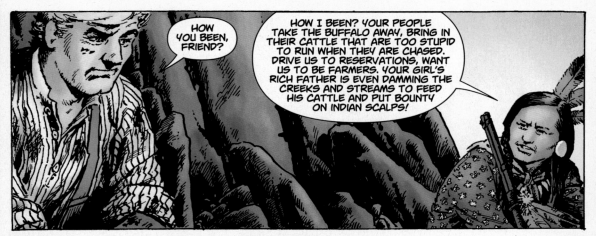

HOW YOU BEEN, FRIEND?

HOW I BEEN? YOUR PEOPLE TAKE THE BUFFALO AWAY, BRING IN THEIR CATTLE THAT ARE TOO STUPID TO RUN WHEN THEY ARE CHASED. DRIVE US TO RESERVATIONS, WANT US TO BE FARMERS. YOUR GIRL'S RICH FATHER IS EVEN DAMMING THE CREEKS AND STREAMS TO FEED HIS CATTLE AND PUT BOUNTY ON INDIAN SCALPS!

YEAH, WILDER'S STILL TRYIN' TO DRIVE MY FOLKS OFF *OUR* LAND, THOUGH WE HAVE AS MUCH RIGHT TO THIS RANGE AS HE DOES. OUR MUSTANGS DO A LOT LESS DAMAGE TO THE STREAMS THAN HIS *SLOW ELK*, TOO!

HE HAS BECOME, TO USE YOUR WORDS, TOO BIG FOR HIS BRITCHES!

ONLY PROBLEM IS, THE LAND-GRABBIN' OLD BASTARD HAS FORTY MEN ON HIS 'ROLL, AND SHERIFF BRUBAKER, WHO'S GOT HIS HAT SET FOR DOMINIQUE, CALLIN' THE SHOTS. BESIDES, MA'S DETERMINED WE'RE ALL GONNA LIVE HERE IN PEACE.

STOP BREAKING MUSTANGS FOR THE ARMY, BAT LASH. COME LIVE WITH COMANCHE. FIGHT WITH COMANCHE. COMANCHE GIRLS WOULD LOVE TO RUN THEIR HANDS THROUGH YOUR TUMBLEWEED HAIR!

IT'S THE FOREVER SLEEPIN' ON THE HARD GROUND I COULDN'T GET USED TO.

THINK I'LL SLIP IN THE BACK IN CASE FATHER AND THE SHERIFF ARE IN THE PARLOR.

JUST THE THOUGHT OF BRUBAKER...MAKES MY SKIN CRAWL.

LET ME GET THIS STRAIGHT...

...YOU SAW BAT LASH WITH MY *DAUGHTER?* OUT ON THE RANGE? *TOGETHER?*

SURE AS TEQUILA ON A BEAN-EATER'S BREATH.

UH... SORRY...

I THOUGHT WE HAD AN AGREEMENT. YOU KEEP THAT DAUGHTER OF YOURS AWAY FROM BAT LASH, AND I SEE TO IT YOU'RE GIVEN EXTRA **CONSIDERATION** IN YOUR WAR AGAINST THE SQUATTERS AND PROSPECTORS.

VICENTE, LEAVE US, PLEASE.

SI, *PATRÓN.*

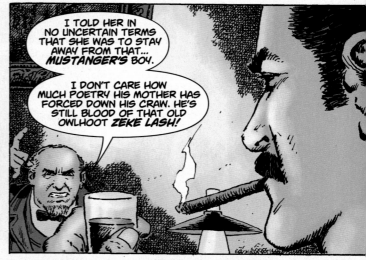

I TOLD HER IN NO UNCERTAIN TERMS THAT SHE WAS TO STAY AWAY FROM THAT... *MUSTANGER'S* BOY.

I DON'T CARE HOW MUCH POETRY HIS MOTHER HAS FORCED DOWN HIS CRAW. HE'S STILL BLOOD OF THAT OLD OWLHOOT *ZEKE LASH!*

WELL, I DAMN NEAR MADE IT EASY FOR HER. LASH'D STILL BE HANGIN' FROM THAT COTTONWOOD UP DAVIS GULCH IF THOSE COMANCHES HADN'T SHOT HIM DOWN.

THOSE DIRT-WORSHIPPERS KILLED EVERY ONE OF MY MEN.

LASH GET A GOOD LOOK AT YOU?

HE'LL REMEMBER MY FACE ON HIS DEATH BED.

THEN YOU'LL HAVE TO GET RID OF HIM. DO IT SOON. IN FACT, TAKE OUT THEIR WHOLE DAMN RANCH. I'VE GIVEN HIS STUBBORN FATHER MORE THAN ENOUGH TIME TO PULL HIS PICKET PIN AND RIDE THE HELL OUT OF HERE!

WHAT ABOUT, UH... *MISSUS LASH?*

SHE CHOSE HER FATE A LONG TIME AGO.

IN THE MEANTIME, I THINK IT'S TIME WE *BOTH* HAD A LITTLE TALK WITH YOUR DAUGHTER.

I WILL SPEAK WITH DOMINIQUE *PRIVATELY.*

IT'S TIME WE *BOTH* TALKED TO HER. I'VE SEEN HOW SHE RESPECTS YOUR ORDERS. IT'S TIME SHE LEARNS TO RESPECT THE WISHES OF THE MAN SHE'S SOON TO MARRY!

PERHAPS. BUT I WARN YOU, YOU HAVE YOUR WORK CUT OUT FOR YOU.

VICENTE!

SUMMON DOMINIQUE FOR ME, *POR FAVOR...*

23

LASH RANCH

PA, BAT'S RIDIN' IN!

FOR THE LOVE OF PETE, BOY, WHERE YOU BEEN? YOU MISSED SUPPER, AND YOUR MA'S FIT TO BE TIED!

SÍ! I THOUGHT FOR CERTAIN THE ANGELS HAD TAKEN MY OLDEST BOY!

I DOUBT THE ANGELS WOULD WANT THIS ONE, MOTHER.

24

WHERE YOU BEEN, BAT? HOW'D YOU GET YOUR CLOTHES ALL TORN?

WALK OL' AMARILLO AROUND A LITTLE, WILL YOU, BILLY? DON'T LET HIM HAVE ANOTHER DRINK TILL HE'S COOLED DOWN GOOD, THEN RUB HIM DOWN AN' GRAIN HIM.

LET'S HAVE IT. IF YOU AIN'T BEEN DRAGGED, I'M A MONKEY'S UNCLE.

YOU AIN'T GONNA LIKE IT, PA.

WILDER'S WOOLIES?

BRUBAKER.

LET'S GO INSIDE. YOUR MA'S GOT WINE AND FRESH *CARNE ASADE*. SHE'LL FEED YA AND TEND THOSE SCRAPES. I WANNA HEAR WHAT HAPPENED OUT THERE.

LIKE I SAID, YOU AIN'T GONNA LIKE IT, PA.

I DON'T DOUBT IT A BIT.

LET'S LIFT SOME GRAVEL, TECUMSEH. I HAVE TO GET TO BAT. I HAVE TO KNOW HE'S ALL RIGHT. HAVE TO WARN HIM...

I KEEP FEELING LIKE SOMEONE'S FOLLOWING ME, BUT NO ONE SAW ME LEAVE THE RANCH...

I'M SURE FATHER KNOWS I'M GONE, BUT HE COULDN'T HAVE CAUGHT UP TO ME. I HAVE TOO MUCH HEAD START.

BESIDES, I'M NOT FOLLOWING ANY TRAIL. WHILE FATHER MAY BE MANY THINGS, HE'S NO TRACKER...

NO, FATHER COULDN'T HAVE TRACKED ME...OR CAUGHT UP TO ME. BUT HE COULD HAVE...

BRUBAKER!

HELLO, DARLING!

AIEEEEEE!

MISS YOUR BETROTHED, DID YA?

UNNNHHHH...

NOOOOOO!

I HAD A FEELIN'.

NOT TO WORRY. I WOULDN'T MARRY YOU NOW...AFTER YOU BEEN WITH THAT SQUATTER'S BOY...FOR ALL THE GOLD IN EL DORADO.

WELL, THAT MIGHT BE A BIT OF AN EXAGGERRATION. IT'S JUST THAT I'M REALLY UPSET, YOU SEE, TO FIND OUT MY CHOSEN GAL BEEN CHEATIN'.

NNNNNH.

THIS OLD RANCH WILL MAKE A COZY LITTLE LOVE NEST. I DONE KILLED THE FAMILY THAT LIVED HERE...FOR YOUR OLD MAN...WHO SAID YOU AND ME WERE ONE....

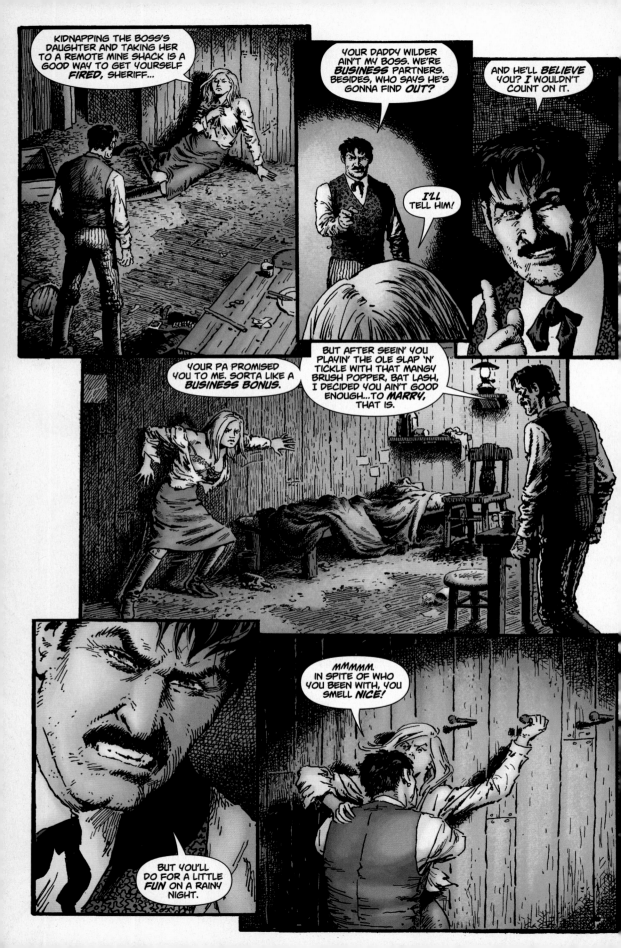

# GUNS AND ROSES

## CHAPTER 2:
## A FLOWER for DOMINIQUE

YOUR WHOLE *FAMILY* CUT YOU OFF, AND LOOK WHAT YOU GOT FOR YOUR *TROUBLE!*

I *HAVE* A FAMILY AND A LOVING HOME. INDEED, IT IS HUMBLE. SO HUMBLE, THAT I AM SURE *YOU* HAVE NO NEED FOR IT. NOW, RIDE OUT OF HERE, AND LEAVE MY FAMILY IN PEACE.

I RECKON YOU ALREADY KNOW MY POSITION ON *THAT* ARGUMENT, MARINA. BUT I DIDN'T COME HERE TO TALK ABOUT OUR *LAND* DISPUTE. I CAME TO BRING MY *DAUGHTER* HOME.

WHAT'RE YOU TALKIN' ABOUT? DOMINIQUE AIN'T HERE!

DAMN YOU, BOY, I KNOW BETTER!

DOMINIQUE IS NOT HERE, GAVIN! WHAT MAKES YOU THINK SO?

THE SHERIFF TOLD ME ABOUT HER AND YOUR BOY GETTING TOGETHER ON THE *SLY* YESTERDAY AFTERNOON. DOMINIQUE CAME HOME, LEFT AGAIN A LITTLE LATER. NEVER *RETURNED*.

I ASSURE YOU, GAVIN, DOMINIQUE DID NOT COME *HERE*!

IF NOT, YOUR SON KNOWS WHERE SHE *IS*!

WHERE IS SHE, DAMN YOU? TELL ME, OR SO HELP ME--

KEEP YOUR HANDS OFF ME, MR. WILDER.

NOW, IF DOMINIQUE AIN'T HOME, YOU'RE WASTIN' TIME LOOKIN' FOR HER *HERE*.

WANT I SHOULD *LEARN* HIM TO TALK MORE POLITE, MR. WILDER?

HUH?

KA BLAM

BLAM

YOU LITTLE *BASTARD*!

BLAM

BLAM

HE'S LOOKIN' FOR DOMINIQUE, PA!

WELL, SHE AIN'T HERE. I RUN A MUSTANG RANCH, NOT A DAMN *MILLINERY*.

I RECKON YOU GOT THE DROP *THIS* TIME, LASH. BUT I HOPE TO GOD MY DAUGHTER ISN'T HERE. FOR YOUR SAKE...AND YOUR FAMILY'S SAKE!

FOR YOUR *OWN* SAKE, YOU SON OF A BITCH, YOU BETTER GIT OFF MY LAND AND *STAY* OFF! THERE'S A LOTTA HUNGRY *BUZZARDS* IN THESE PARTS!

ZEKE, FOR THE TIME BEING WE MUST OVERLOOK OUR DIFFERENCES. THE MAN IS LOOKING FOR HIS *DAUGHTER*!

WHERE ELSE MIGHT SHE HAVE GONE, GAVIN? *THINK!* IF SHE'S BEEN MISSING SINCE LAST NIGHT...

WHY'D SHE LEAVE IN THE *FIRST* PLACE?

MY DAUGHTER'S DOINGS ARE NO BUSINESS OF *YOURS*, YOUNG MAN. NOR WILL THEY *EVER* BE!

AS FOR YOU, *LASH*, THIS ISN'T OUR *LAST* MEETING.

YOU DAMN WELL BETTER HOPE IT IS!

OR YOU'LL BE DODGIN' MORE BUMBLEBEES.

AIN'T THAT RIGHT, PA?

THAT'S *ENOUGH*, BILLY. GO INSIDE AND GET CLEANED UP.

I'LL BE RIDIN' OUT, PA. I GOTTA FIND DOMINIQUE.

THIS AIN'T NONE OF YOUR AFFAIR, BAT. WILDER'LL FIND HIS DAUGHTER. YOU RIDE OUT THERE, YOU'LL GET TANGLED UP WITH HIS RANNIES AGAIN!

YOU CANNOT STOP HIM, ZEKE.

WHY NOT?

DENY IT IF YOU WISH, BUT HE LOVES THE GIRL. AS MUCH AS YOU, AT HIS AGE, LOVED THE DAUGHTER OF A CERTAIN DON...

WE'RE IN FOR ONE HELL OF A DUST-UP, AIN'T WE?

WE SHOULD BE USED TO *DUST-UPS* BY NOW, SHOULDN'T WE, *MI AMOR*?

COULDN'T YOU HAVE FOUND A *BETTER* PLACE TO GET STRANDED?

OKAY, IT'S NOT A SAFE PLACE TO PICNIC. COULD WE *GO* NOW?

NEEEEEEYYYYY!

NO! BANJO! GET BACK HERE, *DAMN* YOU!

BAT, WE'RE NOT GONNA OUTRUN THAT BRUIN!

BROKEN ARROW, TEXAS.

FREE BATHS & TEETH PULLED 25 SENTS

RIO GRANDE SALOON
AND PLEASURE PARLOUR

FINEST SPORTIN GURLS IN TEXAS!

COLD BEER

HODGES

P.I.HODGES MGR.

IT'S BEEN ONE LONG, MISERABLE NIGHT, CARMELITA. THOUGHT I WAS GONNA BLEED *DRY* OR DROWN IN A FLOODED *ARROYO* BEFORE I FINALLY HITCHED A *RIDE* ON A PROSPECTOR'S MEAN *MULE!*

PRIVATE

*MADRE MIA!* WHO DID THIS TO YOU, *UH? ISS* A DEEP *WOUND!*

DO ME A FAVOR, WILL YOU, CARMELITA? *POR FAVOR?*

SHUT YOUR DAMN TRAP AND BANDAGE THE WOUND BEFORE I BLEED TO DEATH!

I DON'T KNOW. IT LOOK *BAAAD!* I THINK YOU BETTER HAVE THE *DOCTOR* SEW YOU UP.

BELIEVE ME, GIRL. YOU WEREN'T MY FIRST CHOICE. DOC WILLIAMS HASN'T GOTTEN BACK FROM SABER GULCH YET. IT'S JUST YOU AND ME, HON. DON'T SCREW IT UP AND MAKE ME ANGRY!

DON'T TUMBLE FOR THE TWENTY-FIVE-CENT TOOTH-PULLIN'. THEY SOAK YE FOR THE TEQUILA IT TAKES TO DEADEN THE PAIN. AND, BELIEVE ME, THERE'S A *LOT* OF PAIN!

YEAH, I DONE LEARNED THAT THE *HARD* WAY.

YOU MEN STAY PUT. JUST ME AND HANEY ARE GOIN' IN. I CATCH ONE OF YOU INSIDE THAT SALOON, YOU'LL BE DRAWING YOUR LAST PAY! WE GOT MORE GROUND TO COVER, AND I WANT YOUR HEADS CLEAR.

CRAP. IT AIN'T THAT OFTEN WE GET TO TOWN.

SHERIFF, ARE YOU IN THERE? IT'S *WILDER!*

KNOCK-KNOCK

CRUD! I WONDER IF HIS DAUGHTER FOUND HER WAY HOME IN THE RAIN...ON *MY* HORSE!

DON'T GET YOUR SHORTS IN A TWIST-- I'M *COMIN'!*

I'M SUCH A DUNDERHEAD SOMETIMES. WELL, IF THE GIRL TOLD WILDER WHAT HAPPENED, AND HE'S COMIN' FER BLOOD, I'LL JUST HAVE TO POP HIM, THAT'S ALL.

WHAT THE HELL ARE YOU DOING HERE, SHERIFF? WE WERE ALL SUPPOSED TO RENDEZVOUS BACK AT MY PLACE. DID YOU FIND MY DAUGHTER?

*Uh*...NO. NO, I DIDN'T.

KIND OF A MESS IN THERE. I RAN INTO TROUBLE OUT ON THE TRAIL. AN OLD OWLHOOT BUSHWHACKED ME. FEELIN' BETTER NOW, THOUGH.

HANEY, WHY DON'T YOU JUST *PRETEND* YOU WASN'T BORN IN A BARN AND USE AN ASHTRAY. THEM *CARPETS* HAPPEN TO BE *TURKISH.*

WELL, PARDON ME ALL TO HELL, SHERIFF. I DON'T SEE AN *ASHTRAY* HEREABOUT.

USE YOUR *HAT.*

IT'LL BURN A *HOLE* IN IT. WHILE IT AIN'T NEAR AS *FANCY* AS *YOUR* HAT, IT DOES HAVE SENTIMENTAL VALUE.

YOU'RE FISHIN' KINDA CLOSE TO THE BOTTOM, AIN'T YA?

A HABIT I CAN'T SEEM TO *BREAK.*

I ADMIT HE'S GOT THE STYLE OF A COONHOUND, AND HE'S DUMBER'N A WAGONLOAD OF CORDWOOD, BUT HE FOLLOWS ORDERS *AND HE'S EFFECTIVE.*

BUT RIGHT NOW I'M TRYING TO FIND MY DAUGHTER. AND I'D APPRECIATE YOUR *HELP* IN *FINDING* HER...SINCE YOU ARE, FOR THE TIME BEING, HER *BETROTHED.*

I'LL START LOOKIN' AGAIN AT FIRST LIGHT. IN THE MEANTIME, I'LL KEEP AN EYE OUT IN TOWN...

IS THAT *CARMELITA* IN THERE WITH YA, SHERIFF? I THOUGHT I SMELLED HER PERFUME.

GIVE HER MY *REGARDS,* WILL YA?

WE BEST STAY HERE FOR THE NIGHT, TILL I CAN RUN DOWN MY HORSE. BEAR MIGHT STILL BE AROUND...

WELL, ISN'T THIS *COZY*, MASTER LASH!

QUIT FOOLIN' AROUND, WILL YOU? I'M WORRIED ABOUT YOU. YOU SURE YOU'RE ALL RIGHT?

I'M FINE. IT'S JUST MY ARM, AND IT DOESN'T HURT MUCH ANYMORE. I SUPPOSE I *AM* A LITTLE... UNNERVED.

BRUBAKER... YOU'RE SURE HE DIDN'T...?

RAPE ME? NO. THOUGH IT WASN'T FOR LACK OF TRYING.

I'M *NOT* A MAN OF VIOLENCE, BUT I CAN'T WAIT TO GET MY HANDS ON THAT--

NO, BAT. YOU'RE NOT GOING TO GET YOURSELF KILLED IN THE NAME OF MY HONOR. *FATHER* WILL HANDLE BRUBAKER.

FATHER HAS NEVER REALIZED WHAT A DEVIL THAT LAWMAN IS. HE WILL *NOW*.

WAKE UP, SLEEPYHEAD! TIME TO PULL OUR PICKET PINS AND GET YOUR ARM TENDED.

SINCE WE'RE HEADIN' TO TOWN, I RECKON WE OUGHTA SPIFFY YOU UP A BIT.

M·H·WILLIAMS
M·D·
UPSTAIRS ↑

GUNSMIT

SHE'S GOING TO BE ALL RIGHT, ISN'T SHE, DOC?

I HAD TO PUT HER OUT TO SET THAT ARM. IT WASN'T AS GENTLE OF A TWIST AS SHE CLAIMED...

SHE SAID IT DIDN'T HURT. THAT GIRL'S GOT THE BARK ON, DON'T SHE, DOC?

SHE'LL CERTAINLY MAKE A HARDY WIFE SOME DAY.

GO ON HOME, SON. SHE NEEDS TO SLEEP, AND YOU LOOK LIKE YOU COULD USE SOME REST YOURSELF.

WHY DON'T YOU TAKE THIS? IT FELL OUT OF HER HAIR.

WHAT THE HELL DID YOU DO TO MY DAUGHTER, YOU SON OF A BITCH?

HEY, THERE, BRUSH-POPPER! WE JUST CAME TO INVITE YOU TO YOUR OWN PRIVATE *NECKTIE PARTY!*

LATER THAT SAME DAY...

HELLO, CLANCY. IRMA. MADE A SUPPLY RUN TO TOWN, DID YA?

WON'T YOU STAY FOR TEA?

AIN'T A *SOCIAL* VISIT, MISSUS LASH. WE SWUNG BY TO TELL YOU BRUBAKER AND WILDER DONE HAULED YOUR BOY OFF TO JAIL. LOOKS LIKE THEY BULLET-GRAZED HIM.

WE'RE AWFUL SORRY TO COME BEARING SUCH AWFUL NEWS, MARINA!

HITCH UP A WAGON, ZEKE. I'M GOING WITH YOU!

NO, YOU AIN'T. YOU'RE STAYIN' HERE. YOU AND BILLY STAY IN THE HOUSE IN CASE WILDER SENDS RIDERS. LOAD THE GUNS AND SHUTTER THE WINDOWS!

I'LL BE BACK WITH MY BOY, OR I *WON'T BE BACK!*

WELL, HELLO THERE, MISTER LASH. HAD A FEELIN' YOU MIGHT DROP BY!

PLUG IT, BONE!

WELL, HELLO THERE, MISTER LASH. HAD A FEELIN' YOU MIGHT DROP BY!

PLUG IT, BRUBAKER. WHY IN TARNATION IS MY BOY LOCKED UP IN YOUR JAIL?

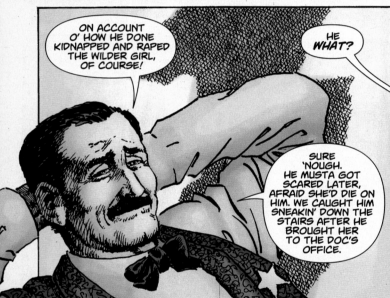

ON ACCOUNT O' HOW HE DONE KIDNAPPED AND RAPED THE WILDER GIRL, OF COURSE!

HE WHAT?

SURE 'NOUGH. HE MUSTA GOT SCARED LATER, AFRAID SHE'D DIE ON HIM. WE CAUGHT HIM SNEAKIN' DOWN THE STAIRS AFTER HE BROUGHT HER TO THE DOC'S OFFICE.

ROUGHED HER UP PRETTY GOOD. HURT HER ARM. HER FATHER'S WITH THE POOR GIRL NOW.

HORSE MANURE! I WANNA SEE MY BOY AN' I WANNA SEE HIM NOW!

BAM

UHH...WELL...THAT WON'T BE POSSIBLE, MISTER LASH. YOU SEE, THE KID TOOK A BULLET ACROSS HIS NOGGIN.

ONE OF MY OWN, TRUTH BE TOLD, AND THE DOC HAD TO PUT HIM OUT TO SEW HIM UP.

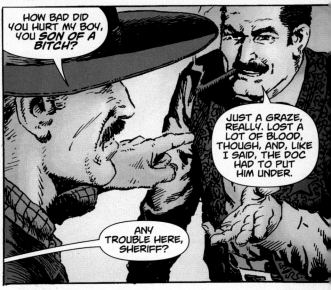

HOW BAD DID YOU HURT MY BOY, YOU *SON OF A BITCH?*

JUST A GRAZE, REALLY. LOST A LOT OF BLOOD, THOUGH, AND, LIKE I SAID, THE DOC HAD TO PUT HIM UNDER.

ANY TROUBLE HERE, SHERIFF?

COME ON, NOW, MISTER LASH. I KNOW IT'S A HARD THING, LEARNIN' YOUR OWN SON'S A *RAPIST,* BUT--

GET YOUR PAWS OFF ME, YOU PRIVY SNIPES!

SMACK!

COFFEE'S READY, YOU SON OF A *BITCH!*

YAHHHH!

CLANG!

YOU LYIN' SON OF A STOCKYARD RAT! BAT WOULDN'T HARM A *HAIR* ON THAT GIRL'S HEAD! I AIN'T LEAVIN' HERE WITHOUT MY *SON!*

I RECKON YOU *ARE!*

OH, BY THE WAY, YOU *CAN* TOMORROW... DURING HIS TRIAL. RIGHT HERE. TEN O'CLOCK SHARP.

DON'T BE LATE OR YOU'LL BE WATCHIN' HIM *HANG!*

WUMP!

THUMP!

KRAK!

KLUD!

PA...?

58

PA, WHAT *HAPPENED?*

EZEKIAL!

BILLY, SADDLE OLD KING. RIDE TOWARD SQUAW CREEK WHILE YOUR MA WRAPS MY RIBS. *FIND TWO-MOONS!*

THE NEXT MORNING...

RISE AN' SHINE, PERVERT. TIME FER A LITTLE NECKTIE SOCIAL... UH...AFTER A FAIR TRIAL, OF COURSE!

PERVERT? DON'T YOU HAVE THAT BACK-ASSWARDS, YOU SCRAP O' RAT DUNG? AND WHAT DO YOU MEAN A *NECKTIE SOCIAL?*

AFTER THE TRIAL, WE'LL TAKE THAT LONG, LAST STROLL...TO THE HANGIN' TREE DOWN BY THE RIVER. ME AND WILDER INTEND TO HOLD A NECKTIE SOCIAL IN *YOUR* HONOR!

THAT THE RAPIST THERE?

ASK YOUR DAUGHTER WHO THE RAPIST IS, MISTER WILDER! ASK *BRUBAKER* HOW HIS *BACK'S* FEELIN' TODAY!

SHUT UP, YOU PRIVY SCUM! THE JUDGE WILL HEAR YOUR CASE AND RENDER HIS OWN VERDICT!

WHOK!

DOGGONE, SON! I *TOLD* YOU WHAT WOULD HAPPEN IF YOU TRIED TO *ESCAPE!*

MEANWHILE, AT THE WILDER RANCH...

HOW MUCH ETHER DID THE DOC GIVE ME, ANYWAY? I FEEL LIKE I'VE BEEN OUT FOR *WEEKS*...

SEÑORITA! THE DOCTOR PRESCRIBED SEVERAL DAYS' BED-REST FOR YOU. I WILL BRING A BREAKFAST TRAY TO YOUR ROOM, *MAS ADELANTE!*

VICENTE, WHERE'S FATHER? I HAVE TO TALK TO HIM RIGHT AWAY.

YOUR FATHER AND SEÑOR HANEY RODE TO BROKEN ARROW FOR A MEETING WITH THE SHERIFF. HE LEFT ORDERS THAT YOU--

WITH THE *SHERIFF?* DOESN'T HE KNOW THAT BRU...?

YOUR FATHER AND THE SHERIFF KNOW *ALL* ABOUT WHAT THAT VILE YOUNG LASH TRIED TO DO TO YOU. IN FACT, THEY'RE MEETING WITH HIM AND THE JUDGE THIS VERY *MORNING!*

THE YOUNG BEAST WILL NO DOUBT BE GETTING HIS *JUST DESSERTS* SHORTLY!

NO, VICENTE! DOESN'T FATHER REALIZE THAT...?

SEÑORITA, *WAIT!*

BAT DIDN'T TRY TO RAPE ME! *BRUBAKER* DID!

DAMN THAT SNAKE TO *HELL!*

SEÑORITA, YOUR WRIST IS HURT, AND YOU'RE BADLY ADDLED. YOU *MUST* STAY IN BED!

LOU, I'M BORROWING CYCLONE!

HEY, LITTLE GAL, WHERE YOU GOIN' WITH MY *HOSS?*

GLUG... GLUG... GLUG...

≡AHH≡ ALL RIGHT, I, JUDGE CLAYMORE P. HICKOCK, DO CALL THIS HERE...UH...*TRIAL* TO ORDER! SHERIFF, WHO'S THE FIRST WITNESS?

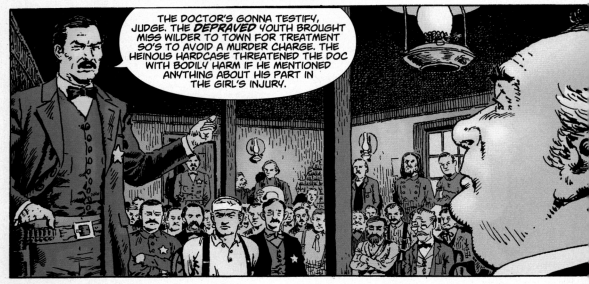

THE DOCTOR'S GONNA TESTIFY, JUDGE. THE *DEPRAVED* YOUTH BROUGHT MISS WILDER TO TOWN FOR TREATMENT SO'S TO AVOID A MURDER CHARGE. THE HEINOUS HARDCASE THREATENED THE DOC WITH BODILY HARM IF HE MENTIONED ANYTHING ABOUT HIS PART IN THE GIRL'S INJURY.

UH...SHE WAS MUTTERING UM...IN HER SLEEP, UNDER THE ETHER. SHE WAS VERY UPSET, SAYING, "BAT, PLEASE...STOP BEFORE YOU GO TOO FAR...!"

THAT'S A *LIE*, DOC, AND YOU *KNOW* IT!

THAT'S ENOUGH, YA DAMN SQUATTER, OR WE'LL STRETCH YOUR NECK *WITHOUT* A TRIAL!

TNK TNK

ANYONE ELSE GONNA TESTIFY? I RECKON THE GIRL SHOULD TELL *HER* SIDE OF IT...

62

FASTER, BOY, FASTER!

BROKEN ARRO[W]
LIVERY & FEED
BARN

HOW CAN I BE SURE...?

YOU AIN'T GOT MUCH CHOICE, NOW, *DO* YA...IF YOU WANT THE LAW ON YOUR SIDE AGAINST THE SQUATTERS...?

YOUR HONOR, MY DAUGHTER INDEED WANTED TO TESTIFY, BUT I'M AFRAID SHE'S JUST TOO *DISTRAUGHT* OVER THE WHOLE AFFAIR.

BUT SHE TOLD ME THAT IT WAS, INDEED, THE SAVAGE YOUNG *LASH* WHO TRIED TO HAVE HIS WAY WITH HER.

HEY, AIN'T THAT THE *BOSS'S DAUGHTER?*

IT *SHOULDN'T* BE! BRUBAKER DONE TOLD ME LAST NIGHT TO KEEP HER THE HELL AWAY FROM TOWN TODAY!

[C]OUSE

[C]OUNTY

I CAN CERTAINLY UNDERSTAND WHY THE POOR CHILD COULDN'T TESTIFY. I'LL ALLOW YOUR TESTIMONY, MISTER WILDER, ON YOUR DAUGHTER'S BEHALF.

WILDER'S AS FULL OF CRAP AS THE SAWBONES, JUDGE! I DIDN'T DO IT, I TELL YA! IT WAS *BRUBAKER!*

HOLD ON, MISS DOMINIQUE.

GRAB THE BRIDLE, BONE!

GET OUT OF THE WAY! I HAVE TO SEE MY *FATHER!*

LET ME GO, DAMN YOU!

I'M REAL SORRY, MISS, BUT YOUR PA'S *REAL BUSY* THIS MORNIN'.

WHAT'S ALL THE COMMOTION OUT THERE?

BAT!

BAAAAAAAAAAAAAAT!

JUST A CRAZY, SYPHILITIC *WHORE*, JUDGE. NOTHIN' TO BOTHER ABOUT.

ALL RIGHT, I'VE HEARD ENOUGH. HE'S GUILTY AS SIN ON THE EVE BEFORE EASTER!

HANG 'IM HIGH AND SEND 'IM UNDER!

HEY, GUESS WHAT? IT'S A NECKTIE PARTY!

JETHRO, RETURN TO YOUR SEAT THIS INSTANT!

WHY, THAT'S BAT LASH. WHAT ON EARTH...?

WHAT'D YOU DO WITH THE GIRL?

TOOK HER OVER TO THE DOC'S. HE'S WITH HER NOW... SEDATING HER AGAIN.

I RECKON YOU OWE ME A LITTLE MORE POCKET JINGLE FOR THAT ONE, SHERIFF...

I *LOVE* YOUR DAUGHTER, MISTER WILDER. AND I'D NEVER DO ANYTHING TO HURT HER. BY NOW, I RECKON YOU'VE FIGURED THAT OUT, *HAVEN'T* YA?

YOU KNOW WHO *REALLY* TRIED TO SAVAGE HER, *DON'T* YA? IT JUST AIN'T *CONVENIENT* FOR *BUSINESS* TO *ADMIT* IT!

SHUT UP, KID! SAVE YOUR LAST AIR FOR *PRAYIN'!*

WHEN THIS TROUBLE IS ALL WRAPPED UP, KILL BRUBAKER. I DON'T CARE HOW. JUST KILL HIM DEADER'N *CUSTER.*

THAT'D JUST TICKLE ME RIGHT DOWN TO MY TOENAILS, BOSS...

RIGGED THAT KNOT SO YOU'LL SUFFOCATE REAL *SLOW,* GIVE YA TIME TO CONSIDER ALL YOUR *SINS* AS YA *KICK!*

WHEN YOU SEE OLE *SCRATCH,* SHAKE HIS HAND FOR ME, WILL YA?

YEAH, AND I'LL TELL HIM YOU'LL BE ALONG *SHORTLY.*

AH, DAMN-- *INJUNZZZ!*

WAP!

SO THAT'S WHY YOU WEREN'T AT THE SO-CALLED *TRIAL*.

I DIDN'T SEE MUCH POINT. YOU SURE YOU'RE ALL RIGHT, SON?

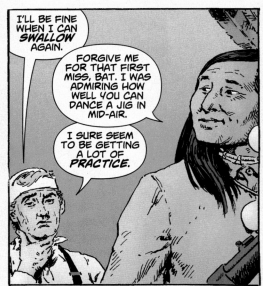

I'LL BE FINE WHEN I CAN *SWALLOW* AGAIN.

FORGIVE ME FOR THAT FIRST MISS, BAT. I WAS ADMIRING HOW WELL YOU CAN DANCE A JIG IN MID-AIR.

I SURE SEEM TO BE GETTING A LOT OF *PRACTICE*.

WE SHOULD'VE RUN WILDER, BRUBAKER, AND ALL THE OTHERS DOWN AND *DRILLED* 'EM!

PROBABLY WOULDA CAUSED MORE *GRIEF* IN THE LONG RUN, PA. ESPECIALLY FOR TWO-MOONS'S PEOPLE.

YOUR MA MADE ME PROMISE TO GO EASY. MAYBE SHE WAS RIGHT. MAYBE WE PUT THE FEAR OF GOD INTO WILDER, AND THE BASTARD'LL DECIDE TO *END* THE FEUD.

YOUR WISHES CLOUD YOUR THINKING, FATHER LASH. IT'S FAR FROM OVER. BRUBAKER AND WILDER WILL VISIT YOUR RANCH WITH THEIR GUN WOLVES. THERE CAN BE *NO* DOUBT.

HE'S RIGHT, PA. WE BEST FETCH MA AND BILLY AND PULL FOOT.

FINE AS FROG HAIR TO ME. YOU FETCH YOUR MA AND BILLY, SON. I'LL STAY WITH THE SPREAD.

IT'S OUR *LAND* HE WANTS. AND TO GET EVEN WITH YOUR MOTHER FOR SPURNING HIM TWENTY YEARS AGO.

WELL, I RECKON WE'VE COME TO A BOX CANYON, AND THERE AIN'T NO WAY OUT BUT FOR *SHOOTIN'*!

HE'S GOT OVER TWENTY MEN ON HIS 'ROLL, PA. AND SOME MEAN AND NASTY *FIREPOWER!*

MY WARRIOR BROTHERS AND I WILL STAY AND FIGHT WITH FATHER LASH AND EVEN THE ODDS. WILDER IS THE COMANCHE'S ENEMY, TOO, BROTHER BAT.

WE WILL KILL THE LAND-HUNGRY WILDER AND BE REWARDED BY THE MOST HOT-BLOODED GIRLS IN THE LAND!

DOES HAWK TALON EVER THINK ABOUT ANYTHING BUT *GIRLS?*

DO YOU?

RECKON YOU GOT ME THERE, TWO-MOONS.

*AGRADEZCA A DIOS!* JESUS HAS SPARED MY SON ONE MORE TIME!

BAT, WE THOUGHT THEY WAS GONNA PLAY *CAT'S CRADLE* WITH YOUR *HEAD!*

I'M FINE, MA, BILLY. AND I HATE TO WORRY YOU AGAIN...

...BUT WILDER'S PROB'LY NOT GONNA ATTACK US TONIGHT. HE'S GONNA MAKE US WAIT AND FIDGET A GOOD, LONG TIME. I'M GONNA RIDE OVER AND SEE IF I CAN'T SPRING DOMINIQUE FROM THE WILDER HOUSE!

DANGIT, BOY, GET BACK HERE!

BAT, *PLEASE,* YOU CAN'T POSSIBLY GET IN AND OUT OF THAT HOUSE WITHOUT WILDER CATCHING YOU!

I GOTTA *TRY,* MA. I'LL BE BACK SHORTLY!

WILDER RANCH

SHH, BOY...YOU WAIT HERE.

I CAN'T QUITE REMEMBER WHERE DOMINIQUE'S BEDROOM IS. BUT PIANO MUSIC'S COMIN' FROM UPSTAIRS.

DOMINIQUE? YOU IN THERE? IT'S BAT.

BAT?

DOMINIQUE, YOU'RE OKAY?

OH, BAT, YOU'RE *ALIVE!*

YOU SHOULDN'T HAVE *COME* HERE, YOU DUMB IDIOT! IF MY FATHER FINDS YOU, HE'LL *KILL* YOU.

I *HAD* TO COME. LAST TIME I SAW YOU...

I TRIED TO GET TO TOWN IN TIME, BUT FATHER'S MEN...HOW DID YOU *EVER* GET AWAY...?

LONG STORY. LET'S JUST SAY BRUBAKER PROBABLY AIN'T ALL THAT HAPPY RIGHT NOW.

BAT, MY FATHER RETURNED FROM TOWN AN HOUR AGO...*ALONE.* I THINK HE MUST HAVE SENT THE OTHERS...

BAT, TAKE ME WITH YOU!

MY FATHER'S A LYING *COWARD.* HE'S *IMPRISONED* ME HERE!

DOMINIQUE, WHAT'S GOING ON IN THERE?

BAM BAM

AS BAT LASH GALLOPS OUT OF THE WILDER RANCHSTEAD, HEADING HOME TO WARN HIS FAMILY THAT SHERIFF BRUBAKER AND A PASSEL OF WILDER'S CUTTHROATS ARE ON THEIR WAY TO WREAK HAVOC...

KELLER, SADDLE ME A FAST HORSE PRONTO! BAT LASH WAS HERE PESTERIN' MY DAUGHTER AGAIN...WHEN HE *SHOULD* BE *HOME*, BURNIN' UP WITH HIS FAMILY!

FATHER, *PLEASE* LET HIM *GO!*

WHAT ABOUT YOUR DAUGHTER, MR. WILDER?

HAVE TUCO LOCK HER IN HER ROOM. CHAIN HER TO HER BED IF HE HAS TO. THERE ARE *HANDCUFFS* IN MY DESK.

WHAT'S ALL THE SHOOTIN' ABOUT, BOSS? I HEARD IT WAY BACK AT THE SECOND CRAPPER!

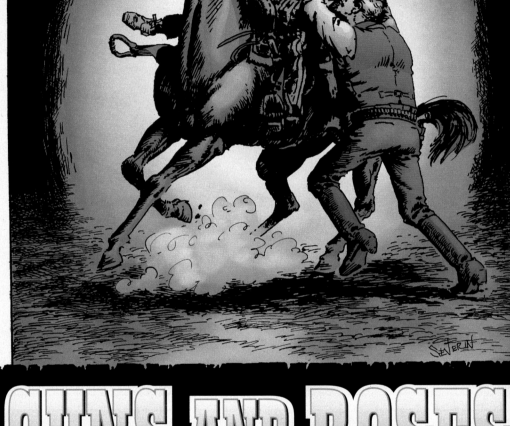

I SURE HATED TO LEAVE DOMINIQUE, BUT...

...GOTTA GET BACK TO THE RANCH...WARN MY FOLKS THAT BRUBAKER AND HIS CURLY WOLVES ARE ON THE WAY...

TONIGHT'S GONNA BE THE END OF NOT ONLY BAT LASH, BUT HIS WHOLE DAMN FAMILY...INCLUDING HIS MOTHER.

MARINA IS FINALLY GOING TO REALIZE HER MISTAKE ALL THOSE YEARS AGO, CHOOSING ZEKE LASH OVER ME.

IT'S SO VERY QUIET, VERDAD?

TOO QUIET, MOTHER LASH.

I SURE WISH YOU'D TAKEN BILLY TO THE NEIGHBORS, HONEY. THINGS ARE GONNA GET WOOLLY AROUND HERE SOON.

MY PLACE IS HERE WITH YOU. IT ALWAYS HAS BEEN. IT ALWAYS WILL BE.

WHERE THE HELL IS BAT? CRAZY DAMN SHAVE-TAIL!

CRAZY IN LOVE...

OUR GUESTS HAVE ARRIVED, FATHER LASH...

LASH, IT'S WAYLON HANEY--GAVIN WILDER'S FOREMAN. BOSS SENT ME TO TALK TO YA. FRIENDLY-LIKE!

WAY I FIGURE, WE AIN'T GOT MUCH TO TALK ABOUT. YOUR BOSS AND BRUBAKER TRIED KILLIN' MY SON TWICE, THE RING-TAILED BOAR COONS!

THAT YOUNG SADDLE TRAMP HAS MORE LIVES THAN A SABER-TOOTHED TIGER, BUT I BELIEVE HE'S DONE USED 'EM UP.

DON'T SHOOT--I'M COMIN' IN. REAL PEACEFUL-LIKE!

HANEY COMES NOT ALONE, FATHER LASH. AT LEAST A DOZEN RIDERS, MAYBE MORE. AND A WAGON...

STAY WHERE YOU ARE, HANEY. YOU AND YOUR BOYS ARE TRESPASSIN' ON PRIVATE PROPERTY!

MARINA, GO ON INSIDE THE HOUSE, HONEY!

HOW MANY TIMES DO I HAVE TO TELL YOU, MI AMOR, I WILL FIGHT BESIDE YOU!

YOU BOYS DO YOURSELVES A FAVOR AND DON'T THROW IN WITH NO MEXICAN WOMEN, HEAR?

I KNOW THAT, MY FLOWER. BUT I NEED YOU INSIDE THE HOUSE IN CASE SOMEONE TRIES TO SNEAK AROUND BACK AND BURN US OUT!

WELL, IN THAT CASE...

WHEW! WASN'T SURE SHE'D FALL FOR IT.

THAT'S FAR ENOUGH, HANEY. WHERE'S THE SON OF A BITCH WHO PULLS YOUR STRINGS?

AND WHERE'S BRUBAKER?

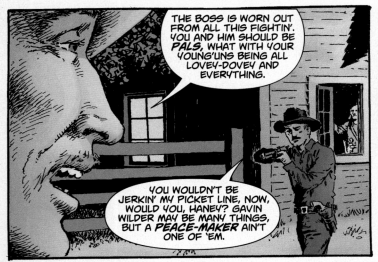

THE BOSS IS WORN OUT FROM ALL THIS FIGHTIN'. YOU AND HIM SHOULD BE *PALS*, WHAT WITH YOUR YOUNG'UNS BEING ALL LOVEY-DOVEY AND EVERYTHING.

YOU WOULDN'T BE JERKIN' MY PICKET LINE, NOW, WOULD YOU, HANEY? GAVIN WILDER MAY BE MANY THINGS, BUT A *PEACE-MAKER* AIN'T ONE OF 'EM.

AS PROOF OF HIS SINCERITY, THE BOSS HAS SENT A SPECIAL GIFT. AND WHEN YOU SEE WHAT IT IS, MR. LASH, YOU'RE GONNA FEEL RIGHT BAD YOU WERE SO SKEPTICAL.

BRING THE WAGON, FELLAS!

WHAT'S GOING ON?

KLIK

WHAT WAS THAT? IT SOUNDED LIKE THE BACK DOOR...

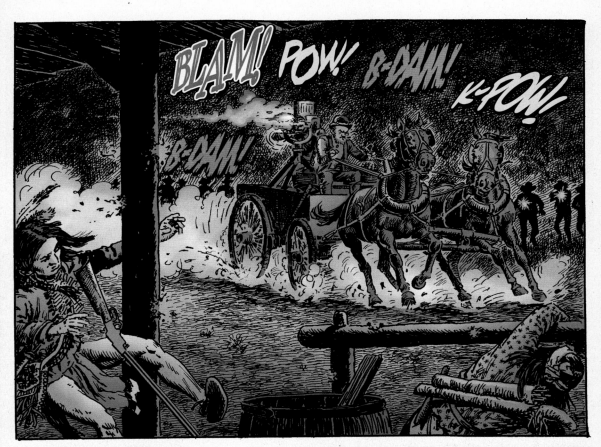

AH, JESUS, GOTTA HURRY!

BLAM! BLAM!

OLD TEXICAN TRICK, PA CALLS IT--PLAYIN' POSSUM!

NEYYYYY!

SOUNDS LIKE I GOT HIM...AT LAST!

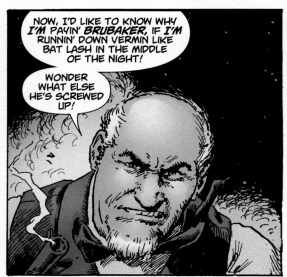

NOW, I'D LIKE TO KNOW WHY I'M PAYIN' BRUBAKER, IF I'M RUNNIN' DOWN VERMIN LIKE BAT LASH IN THE MIDDLE OF THE NIGHT!

WONDER WHAT ELSE HE'S SCREWED UP!

SEE ANY MORE INJUNS AROUND?

NAW, BUT HERE COMES THE BOSS MAN.

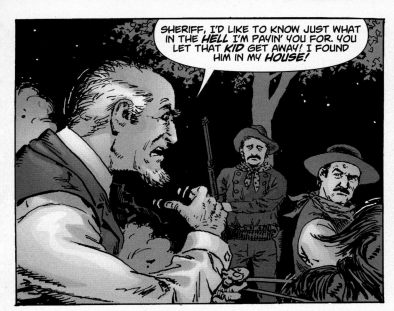

SHERIFF, I'D LIKE TO KNOW JUST WHAT IN THE *HELL* I'M PAYIN' YOU FOR. YOU LET THAT *KID* GET AWAY! I FOUND HIM IN MY *HOUSE!*

BAT LASH!

GILPIN, WADE-- GO SEE IF THE KID'S DEAD. AND I MEAN *DEAD!* POP HIM AGAIN JUST TO BE *SURE!*

MAKE SURE EVERYONE'S DEAD. THEN TORCH THE PLACE!

BOYS, I'M GONNA GET A SCREAM OUTTA THIS REDSKIN YET!

NEXT SCREAM'S COMIN' FROM YOU, HANEY!

BOOM!

BOOM!

BOOM!

YOUR FATHER TAUGHT YOU WELL, BROTHER BAT.

MAYBE *TOO* WELL. SURPRISIN' HOW EASY THAT WAS....

I AM PLEASED YOU FOUND IT EASY, BROTHER BAT.

BAT, YOU MUST KNOW THAT--

I DO KNOW, TWO-MOONS. I'LL GET YOU BACK TO YOUR PEOPLE. THEN I'LL SEE TO MY FAMILY...AND BRUBAKER AND WILDER...

THE NEXT DAY...

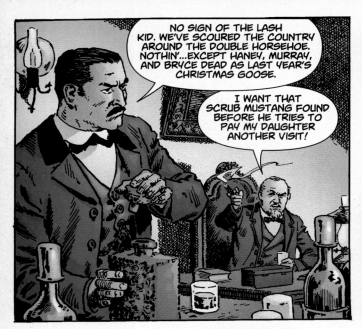

NO SIGN OF THE LASH KID. WE'VE SCOURED THE COUNTRY AROUND THE DOUBLE HORSESHOE. NOTHIN'...EXCEPT HANEY, MURRAY, AND BRYCE DEAD AS LAST YEAR'S CHRISTMAS GOOSE.

I WANT THAT SCRUB MUSTANG FOUND BEFORE HE TRIES TO PAY MY DAUGHTER ANOTHER VISIT!

SORE SHOULDER, SHERIFF?

I'D GET THE DOCTOR TO CHECK IT. THAT NAIL WAS A MITE RUSTY, AND I BURIED IT PRETTY DEEP.

YOU'RE SUPPOSED TO BE IN YOUR ROOM, YOUNG LADY.

THAT PAINS ME MORE THAN THE SHOULDER ITSELF. TO THINK THAT A YOUNG LADY I FELL VERY DEEPLY IN LOVE WITH WOULD BLAME ME FOR WHAT THAT MUSTANGER'S SCRUB OFFSPRING DID TO HER...

I GOT THIS HERE BUM WING HAZIN' DESPERADOES OFF YOUR FATHER'S LAND, YOUNG LADY. AND I'D APPRECIATE A LITTLE GRATITUDE...IF YOU INTEND FOR THE LAW TO CONTINUE BACKIN' YOUR FATHER'S PLAY AGAINST THE BRUSH-POPPIN' SQUATTERS, THAT IS...AND KEEP YOU IN THE STYLE OF LIFE YOU'VE BECOME ACCUSTOMED TO.

BRUBAKER'S RIGHT ABOUT ONE THING, FATHER. YOU HAVE AS MUCH BLOOD ON YOUR HANDS AS HE DOES.

I'M LEAVING. AND I WISH TO NEVER SEE YOU AGAIN AS LONG AS I LIVE.

VICENTE, CALL A COUPLE OF MEN TO THE HOUSE. AND HAVE KELLER BRING THE CARRIAGE AROUND. I WILL BE ACCOMPANYING MY DAUGHTER TO CHIHUAHUA. WILL YOU ALSO SEE THAT SHE'S PACKED ACCORDINGLY?

A SHORT TRIP, SEÑOR?

A *SHORT* TRIP FOR ME. A *LONG* ONE FOR HER. IN FACT, I HAVE NO IDEA *WHEN* SHE'LL BE BACK AGAIN...

*LATER...*

THE NEIGHBORS--CLANCY AND IRMA MILLER--SAW TO THE FOLKS' BURYIN' WHILE I WAS WITH THE COMANCHES. THEY COULDN'T FIND BILLY AMONGST ALL THAT CHARRED RUBBLE. BUT I'M MUCH OBLIGED TO THEM. DON'T THINK I WOULD'VE BEEN UP TO THE TASK...

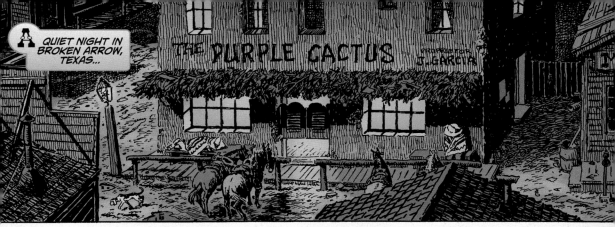

99

# GUNS AND ROSES

CHAPTER 5:

## GUNS ALONG THE RIO BRAVO

*I LEAVE THIS RULE FOR
OTHERS WHEN I'M DEAD--
MAKE SURE YOU'RE RIGHT
THEN GO AHEAD.
--Davy Crockett*

COMANCHE VILLAGE ALONG THE RIO BRAVO.

HEE-YII-HEY-HEY-HEY...!

TUM-TUM
TUM-TUM

AS ALWAYS, I APPRECIATE YOUR PEOPLE'S HELP, TWO-MOONS.

WE ARE BROTHERS, BAT LASH. YOUR TROUBLE IS MY TROUBLE. WHAT WILDER AND BRUBAKER DID TO YOUR RANCH AND YOUR FAMILY MUST NOT REMAIN UNAVENGED.

BESIDES, THEY AND THEIR BELCHING RIFLES KILLED SEVERAL OF MY OWN BROTHERS AND COUSINS. WHEN THE WAR DANCE IS FINISHED, WE WILL VISIT THE WILDER RANCH...

...AND I WILL LEAVE THE PEACE-PIPE HERE.

WE JUST HAVE TO MAKE SURE DOMINIQUE DOESN'T GET HURT. I WANT TO GET HER OUT THE BACK OF THE HOUSE BEFORE THE SHOOTING STARTS.

WE WILL WAIT FOR YOUR SIGNAL. UNTIL THEN, WE WILL TRY TO DRAW AS MANY OF WILDER'S MEN FROM THE RANCH AS POSSIBLE.

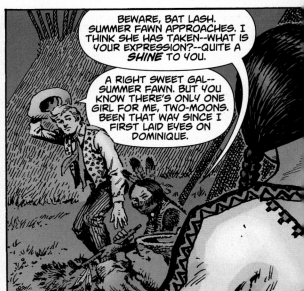

BEWARE, BAT LASH. SUMMER FAWN APPROACHES. I THINK SHE HAS TAKEN--WHAT IS YOUR EXPRESSION?--QUITE A SHINE TO YOU.

A RIGHT SWEET GAL-- SUMMER FAWN. BUT YOU KNOW THERE'S ONLY ONE GIRL FOR ME, TWO-MOONS. BEEN THAT WAY SINCE I FIRST LAID EYES ON DOMINIQUE.

GRANDMOTHER SAYS YOU SHOULD HAVE MORE TEA, BAT LASH...SO YOU WILL CONTINUE TO HEAL.

THANKS JUST THE SAME, SUMMER FAWN. BUT I THINK I'VE DONE ALL THE HEALIN' I CAN FOR NOW.

I'M GONNA TAKE A LITTLE STROLL ALONG THE RIVER, TWO-MOONS. NEED TO SORT OUT MY THOUGHTS BEFORE WE RIDE.

CAN'T GET MY MIND AROUND IT. MA, PA, BILLY...MY WHOLE FAMILY...

DEAD.

YOUR REWARD, INDEED. A FLOWER FOR YOUR HAT, MASTER LASH!

ONLY A FEW WEEKS AGO, ME AND DOMINIQUE RACED ACROSS THIS VERY RIVER...LAID DOWN TOGETHER OVER THERE IN THE SAGE.

HEAVEN ON EARTH IT WAS, SUCH A SHORT TIME AGO.

NOW MA, PA, AND BILLY ARE GONE. MURDERED. THE RANCH IS BURNED. AND ALL I HAVE BETWEEN ME AND HELL IS DOMINIQUE.

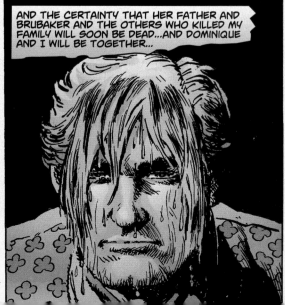

AND THE CERTAINTY THAT HER FATHER AND BRUBAKER AND THE OTHERS WHO KILLED MY FAMILY WILL SOON BE DEAD...AND DOMINIQUE AND I WILL BE TOGETHER...

LUPINE. THE FIRST FLOWER HE EVER GAVE ME...

HE SAID IT WAS THE SAME BLUE AS MY EYES.

FATHER HAS NO RIGHT TO KEEP ME LOCKED IN HERE LIKE A RABID DOG. I CAN'T STAND THE WAITING, THE WONDERING IF BAT ESCAPED HIS PARENTS' FATE!

IF HE ESCAPED MY FATHER AND BRUBAKER!

I'M NOT SURE I CAN DO THIS WITH ONLY ONE ARM, BUT HERE GOES...!

IF BAT'S ALIVE, HE'LL BE WITH TWO-MOONS.

MADE IT!

NOW, FOR A HORSE.

IF FATHER CATCHES ME, I WON'T BE ABLE TO TALK MY WAY OUT OF THE CONVENT THIS TIME!

EASY, CRAZY ANN. EASY...

TUPOLO, SADDLE ME A HORSE. I WANT TO RIDE OUT AND HAVE A LOOK AT THAT INDIAN ENCAMPMENT.

YOU GOT IT, BOSS!

HI-YAAH, CRAZY ANN!

EASY, NOW, MISS. WHERE YOU THINK YOU'RE GOIN'?!

NO!

STOP HER, TOOP!

NEYYY!

VICENTE, I WANT DOMINIQUE LOCKED UP IN MRS. WILDER'S OLD ROOM.

TAKE AWAY HER SLING TOO. HER ARM'S NOT BROKEN, BUT MAYBE THE WRENCH WILL SLOW HER DOWN NOW.

NOT ONLY IS IT FITTING, GIVEN HER BULLHEADEDNESS, BUT IT'LL MAKE IT HARDER FOR THAT MUSTANGER'S BOY TO FIND HER, IF HE COMES CATTIN' AROUND AGAIN!

IF YOU INSIST, DON WILDER!

PUT ME DOWN, YOU DAMN BABOON!

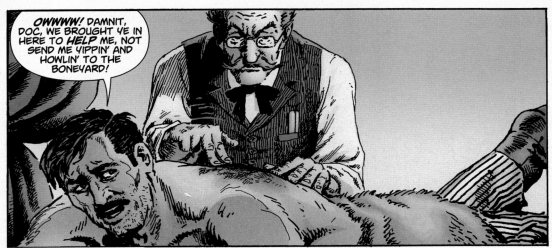

OWWWW! DAMNIT, DOC, WE BROUGHT YE IN HERE TO *HELP* ME, NOT SEND ME YIPPIN' AND HOWLIN' TO THE BONEYARD!

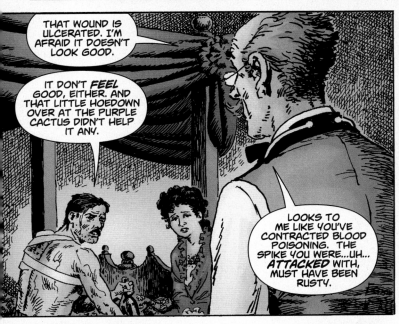

THAT WOUND IS ULCERATED. I'M AFRAID IT DOESN'T LOOK GOOD.

IT DON'T *FEEL* GOOD, EITHER. AND THAT LITTLE HOEDOWN OVER AT THE PURPLE CACTUS DIDN'T HELP IT ANY.

LOOKS TO ME LIKE YOU'VE CONTRACTED BLOOD POISONING. THE SPIKE YOU WERE...UH... *ATTACKED* WITH, MUST HAVE BEEN RUSTY.

NEXT TIME, I'LL TELL HER TO BOIL IT FIRST.

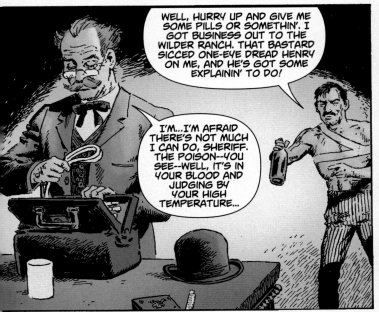

WELL, HURRY UP AND GIVE ME SOME PILLS OR SOMETHIN'. I GOT BUSINESS OUT TO THE WILDER RANCH. THAT BASTARD SICCED ONE-EYE DREAD HENRY ON ME, AND HE'S GOT SOME EXPLAININ' TO DO!

I'M...I'M AFRAID THERE'S NOT MUCH I CAN DO, SHERIFF. THE POISON--YOU SEE--WELL, IT'S IN YOUR BLOOD AND JUDGING BY YOUR HIGH TEMPERATURE...

...THE ONLY THING I CAN PRESCRIBE AT THIS POINT IS BED REST. AND I'M AFRAID I CAN'T, WITH ANY REAL CERTAINTY, GUARANTEE EVEN THAT WILL PULL YOU THROUGH.

YOU LYIN' SACK O' SHEEP DIP, GET THE HELL OUTTA MY ROOM!

JUST LIKE EVERYONE ELSE IN THIS WART-ON-THE-DEVIL'S-BACKSIDE OF A TOWN, YOU'VE TURNED AGAINST ME!

QUACK!

I KNOW WHAT WILL MAKE YOU FEEL BETTER, SHERIFF. IT'S ALWAYS DONE THE TRICK IN THE PAST, HUH?

DON'T BE A FOOL, GIRL. I AIN'T IN THE MOOD FOR BUSINESS.

NEED YOU TO GO TELL THE BOYS IN THE LIVERY BARN TO SADDLE MY HORSE, PRONTO.

AND TELL 'EM TO FETCH MY WINCHESTER FROM THE JAILHOUSE...WITH PLENTY OF AMMO. I GOT HELL TO PAVE AND NO HOT PITCH!

I AM NOT YOUR ERRAND GIRL!

ZING!

ZING!

BLAM!

BLAM!

AHHHHHHHHH!

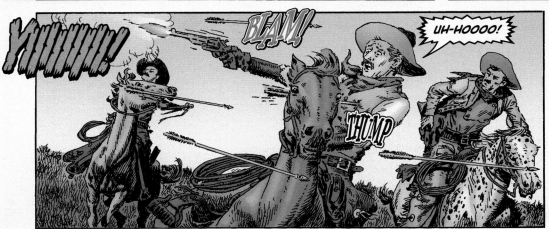

THE TWO CONSPIRATORS SEEM TO BE CONSPIRING *AGAINST* EACH OTHER.

LIKE TWO BULLS IN THE SAME BARN...

COME OUT, COME OUT, WHEREVER YOU ARE, WILDER!

HELLO, KITTEN! STEPPIN' OUT ON ME AGAIN, EH?

LITTLE *BITCH!*

GET DOWN!

*BLAM!*

*K-POW!*

DAMN! HE'S GETTIN' A MITE TOO CLOSE THERE!

*BLAM!*
*BLAM!*
*BLAM!*

HE MUST HAVE SET SEVERAL FIRES. THE HOUSE IS GOING TO GO UP LIKE A TINDER BOX!

HOLD IT RIGHT THERE, LASH!

UHH!

BAT, DON'T!

THINK ABOUT YOUR MA, BOY. WHAT WOULD *SHE* WANT YOU TO DO?

HOW DARE YOU BRING UP MY MA, YOU BASTARD. YOU *MURDERED* HER AN' PA AN' BILLY!

I REGRET WHAT I DID. I...I *LOVED* YOUR MA!

DOMINIQUE, LOOK OUT!

CREEAK!

CRASH!

COUGH!

COUGH!

I'M GOING AFTER WILDER! A JUDGE AND JURY WILL DECIDE *HIS* FATE!

YOU TAKE THIS. IF BRUBAKER SHOWS, *SHOOT* HIM!

THIS OUGHTA PUT ME RIGHT IN HIS PATH!

I'VE GOT YOU NOW, YOU OLD MOSSY-HORN--

--UGH!

OHHHHH... JEEPERS!

HEE-YAH!

OH...

I'M SORRY, MARINA, BUT...

K-POW!

AHH!

NEHH!

HE WAS GOING TO SHOOT YOU, BAT. I...I *HAD* TO KILL HIM...!

SHHH. I LOVE YOU, DOMINIQUE.

I LOVE YOU, BAT!

MOST OF WILDER'S MEN ARE DEAD, BROTHER BAT. A FEW OTHERS ARE FLEEING. WE WILL RIDE THEM DOWN IF YOU WISH.

LET THEM GO, TWO-MOONS.

THE HOUSE, I AM SORRY TO SAY, MISS DOMINIQUE, IS BURNING OUT OF CONTROL.

LET IT BURN.

BRUBAKER!

YOU GO WITH TWO-MOONS, HONEY. HE'LL TAKE GOOD CARE OF YOU TILL I COME BACK FOR YOU.

YOU COULD LET HIM GO, BAT.

123

GET AWAY FROM THERE, SHERIFF. WHEN YOU BURNED THE LASHES OUT, YOU DONE GAVE UP YOUR WATER RIGHTS, FAR AS I'M CONCERNED.

YOU GONE LOCO, YOU STUPID BASTARD? WHY, I OUGHTTA--!

YOU'LL *WHAT?* IN CASE YOU DON'T REMEMBER, THE LAST OF YOUR DEPUTIES INCURRED A BAD CASE OF LEAD POISONING OVER AT THE PURPLE CACTUS. WHY, THE SWAMPER'S STILL MOPPIN' 'EM OFF THE FLOOR.

UH-UH. YOU DONE BEEN BARRED FROM FOULIN' MY WATER, TOO, SHERIFF. FACE IT--YOU'RE OUTGUNNED. NOBODY WANTS YOU HERE. I'D VAMOOSE IF'N I WAS YOU. I'D VAMOOSE *PRONTO!*

YEAH, I'D VA-VAMOOSE PR-PRONTO IF-IF-IF'N I W-WAS YOU, SH-SH-SH-ERIFF!

SHUT YOUR STUTTERIN' TRAP AND GO HEAT SOME WATER, BEAN!

JASON GONSHOR BOOKS

KEEP MOVIN', SHERIFF. YOU DONE PLAYED OUT YOUR HAND IN BROKEN ARROW.

WANT TO GET THIS OVER WITH QUICK. GOTTA GET BACK TO MY GIRL.

POOR DOMINIQUE...SHOT HER OWN FATHER TO SAVE MY WORTHLESS HIDE. GOTTA MAKE IT UP TO HER SOMEHOW...

WHAT'S BRUBAKER UP TO, ANYWAY? HIS TRAIL LEADS RIGHT TO TOWN. I FIGURED HE'D HEAD FOR BROKEN COUNTRY, AMBUSH ME WHERE NO ONE ELSE COULD SEE!

BRUBAKER'S BRASSY, BUT HE WOULDN'T BUSHWHACK ME RIGHT OUT HERE ON THE STREET, WOULD HE?

K·EMERY

WHY, IT'S BAT LASH!

WE KINDA FIGGERED YOU DIED WITH YOUR FAMILY, BAT!

I WAS SPARED, NO THANKS TO THE GOOD SHERIFF.

SPEAKING OF WHOM, EITHER OF YOU SEEN BRUBAKER?

SURE ENOUGH, WE DID. JUST BEFORE HE LIT A SHUCK STRAIGHT WEST.

LIKE SOMEONE HAD SET FIRE TO HIS HOSS'S TAIL!

IF YOU'RE LOOKIN' FER BRUBAKER, BAT, I JUST SEEN HIM. HALF-MILE OUT. HE WAS TURNIN' ONTO THE STAGE TRAIL, HEADIN' SOUTH TOWARD OLD MEXICO!

MUCH OBLIGED, MR. WENTZ!

I APPRECIATE THE OFFER TO TAKE ME BACK TO YOUR VILLAGE, TWO-MOONS.

YOU ARE BAT LASH'S WOMAN, SO YOU WILL BE TREATED AS WELL AS MY OWN SISTERS, I ASSURE YOU.

I'M MUCH OBLIGED TO YOU, TWO-MOONS. BUT I REALLY FEEL LIKE I NEED TO BE ALONE FOR A WHILE.

I RESPECT YOUR WISHES, DOMINIQUE. BUT REMEMBER, IF YOU HAD NOT SHOT YOUR FATHER, YOUR FATHER WOULD HAVE KILLED BAT.

I KNOW THAT. BUT IT'S JUST A *DAMN* HARD THING TO GET USED TO, TWO-MOONS. KNOWING I *MURDERED* MY OWN *FATHER*...!

THERE'S AN OLD SPANISH MISSION AND CONVENT JUST OVER THE BORDER IN CHIHUAHUA. A DAY'S RIDE. I WAS SCHOOLED THERE...AFTER MOTHER LEFT US FOR THE LAST TIME. THE MOTHER SUPERIOR IS AN OLD FRIEND...

I UNDERSTAND, BUT YOU MUST NOT RIDE ALONE. I--

I *MUST*.

"PLEASE LET BAT KNOW WHERE HE CAN FIND ME, WILL YOU, TWO-MOONS?"

BRUBAKER'S HEADIN' TO MEXICO, SURE ENOUGH. HIS TRACKS DISAPPEAR IN THE RIO GRANDE, COME OUT THE OTHER SIDE YONDER.

I BEST HOLE UP, SPEND THE NIGHT HERE, PICK UP THE TRAIL AGAIN COME MORNIN'.

I SURE HOPE YOU'RE ALL RIGHT, DOMINIQUE. DON'T KNOW WHAT I'D DO *WITHOUT* YOU...

WHAT'S HE DOIN'-- VISITING A MEXICAN BONEYAR--?

HUH?

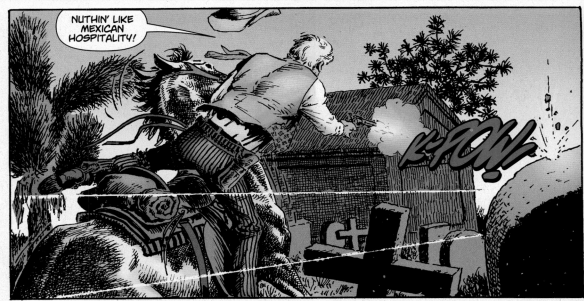

POW!

POW!
POW!

FACE ME LIKE A MAN, YOU BUSHWHACKIN' TINHORN!

MY DAMN AIM'S OFF. I COULDN'T HIT A BULL BUFF RIGHT NOW FROM TWENTY YARDS!

PLUNK!

PLUNK!

MISERABLE DAMN SITUATION...

YELLOW-BELLIED DRYGULCHIN' DEMON! COME BACK AND FACE ME LIKE A MAN, YOU MURDERIN', LAND-GRABBIN' GIRL-SAVAGIN' DAWG!

YOU CAN RUN...BUT YOU SURE AS HELL CAN'T HIDE. NOT EVEN IN MEXICO!

TWO DAYS LATER...

HE'S BACK THERE. CAN'T SEE HIM, BUT I CAN *SMELL* HIM.

NEED...TO GET TO A VILLAGE... ESTANCIA...ANYWHERE I CAN REST FOR A DAY. GET MY STRENGTH BACK...

THE FORK-TAILED DEMON KNOWS HOW TO COVER HIS TRAIL, I'LL GIVE HIM THAT. TWICE NOW I HAD TO BACKTRACK TO PICK IT UP AGAIN.

EASY, MOMMA. I DIDN'T COME DOWN HERE TO HUNT PAINTERS. NO...I COME FOR THE HIDE OF THE MAN WHO MURDERED MY FOLKS AND MY BROTHER, BILLY.

YOU SEEN SUCH A SNAKE AS THAT? I SORTA THOUGHT YA DID...

13

SURE ENOUGH, YA DID. THESE TRACKS ARE 'BOUT TWO HOURS OLD.

ALKALINE AS ALL HELL. STILL, I NEVER TASTED WATER SO *SWEET!*

HUH? WHAT THE--?

SMOKE-TALK! 'PACHES OR YAQUI. DON'T KNOW WHAT'S WORSE.

THAT KID GHOSTIN' MY TRAIL SHOULD BE ALONG JUST ANY OLD TIME. I'LL JUST BUILD A *FIRE* FOR HIM. HE MIGHT WANT TO COOK SOME *COFFEE...*

THEM 'PACHE WILL HOME IN ON MY *COOK FIRE* AN' BURY THAT YOUNG MUSTANGER CHIN-DEEP IN A HILL OF FIRE ANTS SLATHERED IN HONEY. CUT OFF HIS EYELIDS SO THE SUN'LL PARBOIL HIS EYEBALLS WHILE THE ANTS DEVOUR HIM *REAL SLOW!*

HE'S BAITIN' APACHES IN ON ME, AIN'T HE?

AYEEEEEE!!

WHERE--?

HKE-AYY-EEE!!

HNNNGHHAH!

NA-LONGA!

PA-CHOO! PA-CHOO!

MAYBE I CAN FIND *SOMETHIN'* THAT RESEMBLES A HORSE IN THIS LITTLE *JERKWATER.*

WAKE UP THERE, PEDRO. HAVE YOU NO SHAME, BEIN' SEEN IN SUCH RAGS?

ZZZZZ

TINHORN KILLED A GOOD HOSS. AT LEAST WE'VE COME TO THE END OF OUR TRAIL. TIME FOR A *RECKONIN'...*

NOW, *VAMOOSE!*

COME OUT, COME OUT, WHEREVER YOU ARE, YOU SON OF A BITCH...

HOW 'BOUT A LEAD JAWBREAKER, SONNY? RIGHT THROUGH THE *SPINE...*

BLAM!

PLUNK!

CLOSE ONE!

HOLD IT, BRUBAKER!

GRINGO BASTARDS! THINK YOU CAN SHOOT UP MY PLACE, UH?

I SHOW YOU WHAT HAPPENS WHEN YOU BRING TROUBLE TO THE HOUSE OF SEÑORA CLEMENTINA!

EASY WITH THAT THING, LADY!

HEY, MYERS, AIN'T THAT SHERIFF BRUBAKER FROM UP IN BROKEN ARROW?

SURE 'NOUGH, IT IS. LOOKS LIKE HE CAUGHT A RINGTAIL BY THE WRONG END.

I RECOGNIZE THAT RINGTAIL. IT'S THAT OLE SCALAWAG ZEKE LASH'S KID, BAT. MUST BE FOLLOWIN' IN HIS OLD MAN'S FOOTSTEPS!

LOOKS LIKE THE SHERIFF NEEDS A HAND, NICHOLSON!

HOLD IT RIGHT THERE, LASH! DON'T KNOW WHAT LAW YOU BROKE, BUT YOU'RE UNDER ARREST!

K-POW!

BLAM!

THUMP! THUMP!

TURN AROUND, SHERIFF...OR TAKE IT IN THE BACK!

¿QUE PASA?

HA-HA!

EEEEK!

THROW THE GUN DOWN, LASH, OR GET AN INNOCENT PUTA KILLED DEADER'N A BEAVER HAT!

WHO'S THAT WHOREY SMELL REMIND ME OF?

OH, I KNOW. DOMINIQUE!

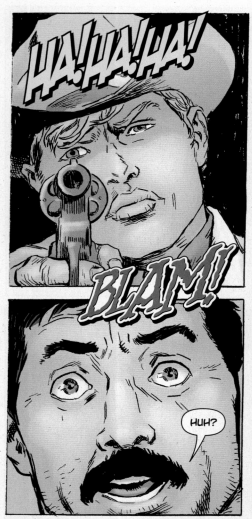

HA! HA! HA!

BLAM!

HUH?

EEEEEEEKKKK!!

CRAASSH!

MADRE MARIA, AND ALL THE SAINTS IN HEAVEN.

DON'T WASTE YOUR PRAYERS, SEÑORITA. IT'S OLE YELLOW-TOOTHED, FORK-TAILED EL DIABLO SHAKIN' THAT MAN'S HAND.

I RECKON I MIGHT HAVE RUBBED THE FUR OF A COUPLA TEXAS RANGERS IN THE WRONG DIRECTION. THERE A BACK WAY OUT OF THIS PLACE?

BROTHER BAT! YOU LIVE! I TRUST YOU ACCOMPLISHED THAT WHICH YOU SET OUT TO DO?

I RECKON YOU COULD SAY THAT, MY BROTHER. BRUBAKER'S WHERE HE BELONGS, AND I GOT A MIGHTY GOOD FEELIN' MY FOLKS AND BILLY ARE RESTIN' SOUNDER.

HOW'S EVERYTHING HERE? NO ONE'S DOGGED YOUR PEOPLE FOR HELPIN' ME WITH WILDER'S GUN WOLVES, HAVE THEY?

I THINK THE FEW WILDER WOLVES STILL STANDING ARE HOLED UP LICKING THEIR WOUNDS, BROTHER BAT. MY PEOPLE ARE PREPARING TO MOVE NOW, FOLLOWING THE LAST OF THE BUFFALO HERDS NORTH FOR THE WINTER.

IN THAT CASE, I'LL FETCH MY GIRL, AND ME AND DOMINIQUE'LL BE OUT OF YOUR HAIR IN NO TIME! I SURE APPRECIATE ALL YOUR HELP, TWO-MOONS. I NEVER COULDA--

HOLD UP, BROTHER BAT. ABOUT DOMINIQUE...

WHAT ABOUT HER?

WELCOME TO SANTA CATARINA, SEÑOR. YOU ARE BAT LASH. I AM SISTER CORAZON...AN OLD FRIEND OF DOMINIQUE'S.

DOMINIQUE... SHE'S HERE, THEN...?

IN THE GARDEN, ON THE OTHER SIDE OF THE MISSION HOUSE. THERE IS A GATE IN THE WALL. I WILL SEND FOR THE STABLE BOY TO TEND YOUR HORSE. HE LOOKS THIRSTY...

D-DOMINIQUE...?

BAT!

WHAT'RE YOU DOING HERE, YOU CRAZY GIRL?

BAT...

IT'S FINISHED, DOMINIQUE. LET'S GO HOME!

I CAN'T GO WITH YOU, BAT.

DON'T YOU SEE--WE DON'T HAVE A HOME! NEITHER OF US! IT'S ALL BEEN TAKEN AWAY FROM US, BAT. OUR PAST, OUR FUTURE, EVERYTHING!

DON'T... DON'T YOU LOVE ME...?

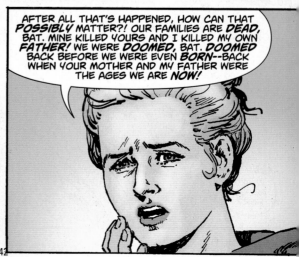

AFTER ALL THAT'S HAPPENED, HOW CAN THAT POSSIBLY MATTER?! OUR FAMILIES ARE DEAD, BAT. MINE KILLED YOURS AND I KILLED MY OWN FATHER! WE WERE DOOMED, BAT. DOOMED BACK BEFORE WE WERE EVEN BORN--BACK WHEN YOUR MOTHER AND MY FATHER WERE THE AGES WE ARE NOW!

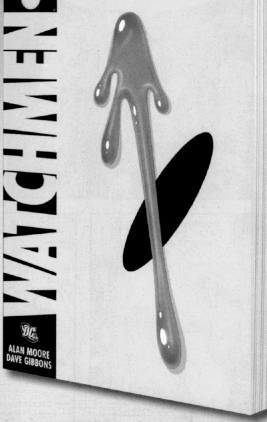